ADDRESSES

Name:

Address:

Home: Mobile:

Email:

Name:

Address:

Home: Mobile:

Email:

Name:

Address:

Home: Mobile:

Email:

Name:

Address:

Home: Mobile:

Email:

Name:

Address:

Home: Mobile:

Email:

Name:

Address:

Home: Mobile:

Email:

Name:

Address:

Home: Mobile:

Email:

Name:

Address:

Home: Mobile:

Email:

Name:

Address:

Home: Mobile:

Email:

Name:

Address:

Home: Mobile:

Email:

Name:

Address:

Home: Mobile:

Email:

Name:

Address:

Home: Mobile:

Email:

Name:

Address:

Home: Mobile:

Email:

Name:

Address:

Home: Mobile:

Email:

Name:

Address:

Home: Mobile:

Email:

Name:

Address:

Home: Mobile:

Email:

Name:

Address:

Home: Mobile:

Email:

Name:

Address:

Home: Mobile:

Email:

Name:

Address:

Home: Mobile:

Email:

Name:

Address:

Home: Mobile:

Email:

Name:

Address:

Home: Mobile:

Email:

Name:

Address:

Home: Mobile:

Email:

Name:

Address:

Home: Mobile:

Email:

Name:

Address:

Home: Mobile:

Email:

Name:

Address:

Home: Mobile:

Email:

Name:

Address:

Home: Mobile:

Email:

Name:

Address:

Home: Mobile:

Email:

Name:

Address:

Home: Mobile:

Email:

Name:

Address:

Home: Mobile:

Email:

Name:

Address:

Home: Mobile:

Email:

Name:

Address:

Home: Mobile:

Email:

Name:

Address:

Home: Mobile:

Email:

Name:

Address:

Home: Mobile:

Email:

Name:

Address:

Home: Mobile:

Email:

Name:

Address:

Home: Mobile:

Email:

Name:

Address:

Home: Mobile:

Email:

Name:

Address:

Home: Mobile:

Email:

Name:

Address:

Home: Mobile:

Email:

Name:

Address:

Home: Mobile:

Email:

Name:

Address:

Home: Mobile:

Email:

Name:

Address:

Home: Mobile:

Email:

Name:

Address:

Home: Mobile:

Email:

Name:

Address:

Home: Mobile:

Email:

Name:

Address:

Home: Mobile:

Email:

Name:

Address:

Home: Mobile:

Email:

Name:

Address:

Home: Mobile:

Email:

Name:

Address:

Home: Mobile:

Email:

Name:

Address:

Home: Mobile:

Email:

Name:

Address:

Home: Mobile:

Email:

Name:

Address:

Home: Mobile:

Email:

Name:

Address:

Home: Mobile:

Email:

Name:

Address:

Home: Mobile:

Email:

Name:

Address:

Home: Mobile:

Email:

Name:

Address:

Home: Mobile:

Email:

Name:

Address:

Home: Mobile:

Email:

Name:

Address:

Home: Mobile:

Email:

Name:

Address:

Home: Mobile:

Email:

Name:

Address:

Home: Mobile:

Email:

Name:

Address:

Home: Mobile:

Email:

Name:

Address:

Home: Mobile:

Email:

Name:

Address:

Home: Mobile:

Email:

Name:

Address:

Home: Mobile:

Email:

Name:

Address:

Home: Mobile:

Email:

Name:

Address:

Home: Mobile:

Email:

Name:

Address:

Home: Mobile:

Email:

Name:

Address:

Home: Mobile:

Email:

Name:

Address:

Home: Mobile:

Email:

Name:

Address:

Home: Mobile:

Email:

Name:

Address:

Home: Mobile:

Email:

Name:

Address:

Home: Mobile:

Email:

Name:

Address:

Home: Mobile:

Email:

Name:

Address:

Home: Mobile:

Email:

Name:

Address:

Home: Mobile:

Email:

G H

Name:

Address:

Home: Mobile:

Email:

Name:

Address:

Home: Mobile:

Email:

Name:

Address:

Home: Mobile:

Email:

Name:

Address:

Home: Mobile:

Email:

Name:

Address:

Home: Mobile:

Email:

Name:

Address:

Home: Mobile:

Email:

Name:

Address:

Home: Mobile:

Email:

Name:

Address:

Home: Mobile:

Email:

Name:

Address:

Home: Mobile:

Email:

Name:

Address:

Home: Mobile:

Email:

Name:

Address:

Home: Mobile:

Email:

Name:

Address:

Home: Mobile:

Email:

Name:

Address:

Home: Mobile:

Email:

Name:

Address:

Home: Mobile:

Email:

Name:

Address:

Home: Mobile:

Email:

Name:

Address:

Home: Mobile:

Email:

Name:

Address:

Home: Mobile:

Email:

Name:

Address:

Home: Mobile:

Email:

G H

Name:

Address:

Home: Mobile:

Email:

Name:

Address:

Home: Mobile:

Email:

Name:

Address:

Home: Mobile:

Email:

Name:

Address:

Home: Mobile:

Email:

Name:

Address:

Home: Mobile:

Email:

Name:

Address:

Home: Mobile:

Email:

Name:

Address:

Home: Mobile:

Email:

Name:

Address:

Home: Mobile:

Email:

Name:

Address:

Home: Mobile:

Email:

Name:

Address:

Home: Mobile:

Email:

Name:

Address:

Home: Mobile:

Email:

Name:

Address:

Home: Mobile:

Email:

Name:

Address:

Home: Mobile:

Email:

Name:

Address:

Home: Mobile:

Email:

Name:

Address:

Home: Mobile:

Email:

Name:

Address:

Home: Mobile:

Email:

Name:

Address:

Home: Mobile:

Email:

Name:

Address:

Home: Mobile:

Email:

Name:

Address:

Home: Mobile:

Email:

Name:

Address:

Home: Mobile:

Email:

Name:

Address:

Home: Mobile:

Email:

Name:

Address:

Home: Mobile:

Email:

Name:

Address:

Home: Mobile:

Email:

Name:

Address:

Home: Mobile:

Email:

Name:

Address:

Home: Mobile:

Email:

Name:

Address:

Home: Mobile:

Email:

Name:

Address:

Home: Mobile:

Email:

Name:

Address:

Home: Mobile:

Email:

Name:

Address:

Home: Mobile:

Email:

Name:

Address:

Home: Mobile:

Email:

Name:

Address: K L

Home: Mobile:

Email:

Name:

Address:

Home: Mobile:

Email:

Name:

Address:

Home: Mobile:

Email:

Name:

Address:

Home: Mobile:

Email:

Name:

Address:

Home: Mobile:

Email:

Name:
Address:

Home: Mobile:
Email:

Name:
Address:

K L

Home: Mobile:
Email:

Name:
Address:

Home: Mobile:
Email:

Name:
Address:

Home: Mobile:
Email:

Name:
Address:

Home: Mobile:
Email:

Name:
Address:

Home: Mobile:
Email:

Name:
Address:

Home: Mobile:
Email:

Name:
Address: K L

Home: Mobile:
Email:

Name:
Address:

Home: Mobile:
Email:

Name:

Address:

Home: Mobile:

Email:

Name:

Address:

Home: Mobile:

Email:

Name:

Address:

Home: Mobile:

Email:

Name:

Address:

Home: Mobile:

Email:

Name:

Address:

Home: Mobile:

Email:

Name:

Address:

Home: Mobile:

Email:

K L

Name:

Address:

Home: Mobile:

Email:

Name:

Address:

Home: Mobile:

Email:

Name:

Address:

Home: Mobile:

Email:

Name:

Address:

Home: Mobile:

Email:

Name:

Address:

Home: Mobile:

Email:

Name:

Address:

Home: Mobile:

Email:

Name:

Address:

Home: Mobile:

Email:

Name:

Address:

Home: Mobile:

Email:

Name:

Address:

Home: Mobile:

Email:

Name:

Address:

Home: Mobile:

Email:

Name:

Address:

Home: Mobile:

Email:

Name:

Address:

Home: Mobile:

Email:

M N

Name:

Address:

Home: Mobile:

Email:

Name:

Address:

Home: Mobile:

Email:

Name:

Address:

Home: Mobile:

Email:

Name:

Address:

Home: Mobile:

Email:

Name:

Address:

Home: Mobile:

Email:

M N

Name:

Address:

Home: Mobile:

Email:

Name:
Address:

Home: Mobile:
Email:

Name:
Address:

Home: Mobile:
Email:

Name:
Address:

Home: Mobile:
Email:

Name:

Address:

Home: Mobile:

Email:

Name:

Address:

Home: Mobile:

Email:

Name:

Address:

Home: Mobile:

Email:

Name:

Address:

Home: Mobile:

Email:

Name:

Address:

Home: Mobile:

Email:

Name:

Address:

Home: Mobile:

Email:

Name:

Address:

Home: Mobile:

Email:

Name:

Address:

Home: Mobile:

Email:

Name:

Address:

Home: Mobile:

Email:

Name:

Address:

Home: Mobile:

Email:

Name:

Address:

Home: Mobile:

Email:

Name:

Address:

Home: Mobile:

Email:

Name:

Address:

Home: Mobile:

Email:

Name:

Address:

Home: Mobile:

Email:

Name:

Address:

Home: Mobile:

Email:

Name:

Address:

Home: Mobile:

Email:

Name:

Address:

Home: Mobile:

Email:

Name:

Address:

Home: Mobile:

Email:

Name:

Address:

Home: Mobile:

Email:

Name:

Address:

Home: Mobile:

Email:

Name:

Address:

Home: Mobile:

Email:

Name:

Address:

Home: Mobile:

Email:

Name:

Address:

Home: Mobile:

Email:

Name:

Address:

Home: Mobile:

Email:

Name:

Address:

Home: Mobile:

Email:

Name:

Address:

Home: Mobile:

Email:

Name:

Address:

Home: Mobile:

Email:

Name:

Address:

Home: Mobile:

Email:

Name:

Address:

Home: Mobile:

Email:

Name:

Address:

Home: Mobile:

Email:

Name:

Address:

Home: Mobile:

Email:

Name:

Address:

Home: Mobile:

Email:

Q R

Name:

Address:

Home: Mobile:

Email:

Name:

Address:

Home: Mobile:

Email:

Name:

Address:

Home: Mobile:

Email:

Name:

Address:

Home: Mobile:

Email:

Name:

Address:

Home: Mobile:

Email:

Name:

Address:

Home: Mobile:

Email:

Name:

Address:

Home: Mobile:

Email:

Name:

Address:

Home: Mobile:

Email:

Name:

Address:

Home: Mobile:

Email:

Name:

Address:

Home: Mobile:

Email:

Name:

Address:

Home: Mobile:

Email:

Name:

Address:

Home: Mobile:

Email:

Name:

Address:

Home: Mobile:

Email:

Name:

Address:

Home: Mobile:

Email:

Name:

Address:

Home: Mobile:

Email:

Name:

Address:

Home: Mobile:

Email:

Name:

Address:

Home: Mobile:

Email:

Name:

Address:

Home: Mobile:

Email:

Name:

Address:

Home: Mobile:

Email:

Name:

Address:

Home: Mobile:

Email:

Name:

Address:

Home: Mobile:

Email:

Name:

Address:

Home: Mobile:

Email:

Name:

Address:

Home: Mobile:

Email:

Name:

Address:

Home: Mobile:

Email:

Name:

Address:

Home: Mobile:

Email:

Name:

Address:

Home: Mobile:

Email:

Name:

Address:

Home: Mobile:

Email:

Name:

Address:

Home: Mobile:

Email:

Name:

Address:

Home: Mobile:

Email:

Name:

Address:

Home: Mobile:

Email:

Name:

Address:

Home: Mobile:

Email:

Name:

Address:

Home: Mobile:

Email:

Name:

Address:

Home: Mobile:

Email:

Name:

Address:

Home: Mobile:

Email:

Name:

Address:

Home: Mobile:

Email:

Name:

Address:

Home: Mobile:

Email:

Name:

Address:

Home: Mobile:

Email:

Name:

Address:

Home: Mobile:

Email:

Name:

Address:

Home: Mobile:

Email:

Name:

Address:

Home: Mobile:

Email:

Name:

Address:

Home: Mobile:

Email:

Name:

Address:

Home: Mobile:

Email:

Name:

Address:

Home: Mobile:

Email:

Name:

Address:

Home: Mobile:

Email:

Name:

Address:

Home: Mobile:

Email:

Name:

Address:

Home: Mobile:

Email:

Name:

Address:

Home: Mobile:

Email:

Name:

Address:

Home: Mobile:

Email:

Name:

Address:

Home: Mobile:

Email:

Name:

Address:

Home: Mobile:

Email:

Name:

Address:

Home: Mobile:

Email:

Name:

Address:

Home: Mobile:

Email:

Name:

Address:

Home: Mobile:

Email:

Name:

Address:

Home: Mobile:

Email:

Name:

Address:

Home: Mobile:

Email:

U V

Name:

Address:

Home: Mobile:

Email:

Name:

Address:

Home: Mobile:

Email:

Name:

Address:

Home: Mobile:

Email:

Name:

Address:

Home: Mobile:

Email:

Name:

Address:

Home: Mobile:

Email:

Name:

Address:

Home: Mobile:

Email:

Name:

Address:

Home: Mobile:

Email:

Name:

Address:

Home: Mobile:

Email:

Name:

Address:

Home: Mobile:

Email:

Name:

Address:

Home: Mobile:

Email:

Name:

Address:

Home: Mobile:

Email:

Name:

Address:

Home: Mobile:

Email:

U V

Name:

Address:

Home: Mobile:

Email:

Name:

Address:

Home: Mobile:

Email:

Name:

Address:

Home: Mobile:

Email:

Name:

Address:

Home: Mobile:

Email:

Name:

Address:

Home: Mobile:

Email:

Name:

Address:

Home: Mobile:

Email:

Name:

Address:

Home: Mobile:

Email:

Name:

Address:

Home: Mobile:

Email:

Name:

Address:

Home: Mobile:

Email:

Name:

Address:

Home: Mobile:

Email:

Name:

Address:

Home: Mobile:

Email:

Name:

Address:

Home: Mobile:

Email:

W X

Name:

Address:

Home: Mobile:

Email:

Name:

Address:

Home: Mobile:

Email:

Name:

Address:

Home: Mobile:

Email:

Name:

Address:

Home: Mobile:

Email:

Name:

Address:

Home: Mobile:

Email:

Name:

Address:

Home: Mobile:

Email:

W X

Name:

Address:

Home: Mobile:

Email:

Name:

Address:

Home: Mobile:

Email:

Name:

Address:

Home: Mobile:

Email:

Name:

Address:

Home: Mobile:

Email:

Name:

Address:

Home: Mobile:

Email:

Name:

Address:

Home: Mobile:

Email:

W X

Name:

Address:

Home: Mobile:

Email:

Name:

Address:

Home: Mobile:

Email:

Name:

Address:

Home: Mobile:

Email:

Name:

Address:

Home: Mobile:

Email:

Name:

Address:

Home: Mobile:

Email:

Name:

Address:

Home: Mobile:

Email:

Name:

Address:

Home: Mobile:

Email:

Name:

Address:

Home: Mobile:

Email:

Name:

Address:

Home: Mobile:

Email:

Name:

Address:

Home: Mobile:

Email:

Name:

Address:

Home: Mobile:

Email:

Name:

Address:

Home: Mobile:

Email:

Y Z

Name:

Address:

Home: Mobile:

Email:

Name:

Address:

Home: Mobile:

Email:

Name:

Address:

Home: Mobile:

Email:

Name:

Address:

Home: Mobile:

Email:

Name:

Address:

Home: Mobile:

Email:

Name:

Address:

Home: Mobile:

Email:

Name:

Address:

Home: Mobile:

Email:

Name:

Address:

Home: Mobile:

Email:

Name:

Address:

Home: Mobile:

Email:

Name:

Address:

Home: Mobile:

Email:

Name:

Address:

Home: Mobile:

Email:

Name:

Address:

Home: Mobile:

Email:

y z

Name:

Address:

Home: Mobile:

Email:

Name:

Address:

Home: Mobile:

Email:

Name:

Address:

Home: Mobile:

Email:

BIRTHDAYS

January

1st

2nd

3rd

4th

January

5th

6th

7th

8th

January

9th

10th

11th

12th

January

13th

14th

15th

16th

January

17th

18th

19th

20th

January

21st

22nd

23rd

24th

January

25th

26th

27th

28th

January

29th

30th

31st

February

1st

2nd

3rd

4th

February

5th

6th

7th

8th

February

9th

10th

11th

12th

February

13th

14th

15th

16th

February

17th

18th

19th

20th

February

21st

22nd

23rd

24th

February

25th

26th

27th

28th

February

29th

March

1st

2nd

3rd

4th

March

5th

6th

7th

8th

March

9th

10th

11th

12th

March

13th

14th

15th

16th

March

17th

18th

19th

20th

March

21st

22nd

23rd

24th

March

25th

26th

27th

28th

March

29th

30th

31st

April

1st

2nd

3rd

4th

April

5th

6th

7th

8th

April

9th

10th

11th

12th

April

13th

14th

15th

16th

April

17th

18th

19th

20th

April

21st

22nd

23rd

24th

April

25th

26th

27th

28th

April

29th

30th

May

1st

2nd

3rd

4th

May

5th

6th

7th

8th

May

9th

10th

11th

12th

May

13th

14th

15th

16th

May

17th

18th

19th

20th

May

21st

22nd

23rd

24th

May

25th

26th

27th

28th

May

29th

30th

31st

June

1st

2nd

3rd

4th

June

5th

6th

7th

8th

June

9th

10th

11th

12th

June

13th

14th

15th

16th

June

17th

18th

19th

20th

June

21st

22nd

23rd

24th

June

25th

26th

27th

28th

June

29th

30th

July

1st

2nd

3rd

4th

July

5th

6th

7th

8th

July

9th

10th

11th

12th

July

13th

14th

15th

16th

July

17th

18th

19th

20th

July

21st

22nd

23rd

24th

July

25th

26th

27th

28th

July

29th

30th

31st

August

1st

2nd

3rd

4th

August

5th

6th

7th

8th

August

9th

10th

11th

12th

August

13th

14th

15th

16th

August

17th

18th

19th

20th

August

21st

22nd

23rd

24th

August

25th.

26th

27th

28th

August

29th

30th

31st

September

1st

2nd

3rd

4th

September

5th

6th

7th

8th

September

9th

10th

11th

12th

September

13th

14th

15th

16th

September

17th

18th

19th

20th

September

21st

22nd

23rd

24th

September

25th

26th

27th

28th

September

29th

30th

October

1st

2nd

3rd

4th

October

5th

6th

7th

8th

October

9th

10th

11th

12th

October

13th

14th

15th

16th

October

17th

18th

19th

20th

October

21st

22nd

23rd

24th

October

25th

26th

27th

28th

October

29th

30th

31st

November

1st

2nd

3rd

4th

November

5th

6th

7th

8th

November

9th

10th

11th

12th

November

13th

14th

15th

16th

November

17th

18th

19th

20th

November

21st

22nd

23rd

24th

November

25th

26th

27th

28th

November

29th

30th

December

1st
....
....
....

2nd
....
....
....

3rd
....
....
....

4th
....
....
....

December

5th

6th

7th

8th

December

9th

10th

11th

12th

December

13th

14th

15th

16th

December

17th

18th

19th

20th

December

21st

22nd

23rd

24th

December

25th

26th

27th

28th

December

29th

30th

31st